After Dark

(To be read by the teacher.)

Running Moon

Sometimes when we drive out at night
I see the half moon, thin and white.
It runs beside us like a hound,
It's there whenever I turn round.

I say "Good moon, come on, good moon!
It won't be long, we'll be home soon,"
And when we stop, there in the sky
The moon stands still, as still as I.

ELIZABETH COATSWORTH

6

Jack's Star

Stan and Jack played.
They played in the grass.
"Look!" said Jack.
"Look at the funny little
lights in the grass."

"They are lightning bugs,"
said Stan.
"Lightning bugs light up.
Then they get dark."

7

Stan ran after a lightning bug.
But he lost it in the dark.
"I'll get a bug," said Jack.
Jack ran after a lightning bug.
"I have it!" said Jack.
"I have it!
Get a box for it, Stan."

But Stan said, "I'll get a jar.
Then we can see the lightning
bug light up."
He ran to get the jar.

Jack put the bug into the jar.
He said, "Look at it light
up, Stan."
They saw the bug light up and
then get dark.

9

Then Jack said, "We have to
go in.

Go away, lightning bug."

The lightning bug went up from
the jar.

It went up into the sky.

Stan said, "Look at the
lightning bug, Jack.

It is a little star in
the dark."

(To be read by the teacher.)

Firefly

A little light is going by,
Is going up to see the sky,
A little light with wings.

I never could have thought of it,
To have a little bug all lit
And made to go on wings.

ELIZABETH MADOX ROBERTS

11

Eyes in the Night

It is night.
A cat is on the hill.
The sky is gray.
But the cat can see.
Cats can not see in the dark.
But they can see in very
little light.
Cats can see in the light
from the stars.

12

This mouse's eyes look very big.

It can see in very little light.

The mouse did not go into the bright morning light.

It did not go into the bright afternoon light.

But it is night.

The mouse can see the cat.

And it can see the owl.

In the night, the mouse's eyes look big.

The owl's eyes look big.

And the cat's eyes look big.

In the night, your eyes look big.

Is that a surprise to you?

You are a little like the mouse, owl, and cat.

You can not see in the dark.

But you can see a little in the light from the stars.

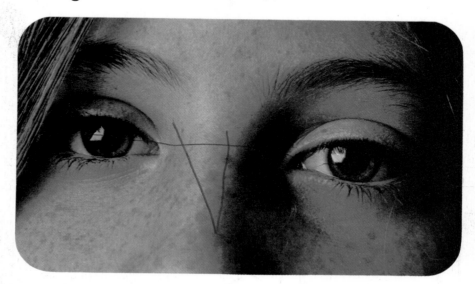

The Sleep Out

Pam and Ted played in the dark.
Then they ran up to Mother.
Ted said, "Please, can Pam
and I sleep out here?"

Mother said, "Yes, you can."

"We will have fun out here,"
said Pam.

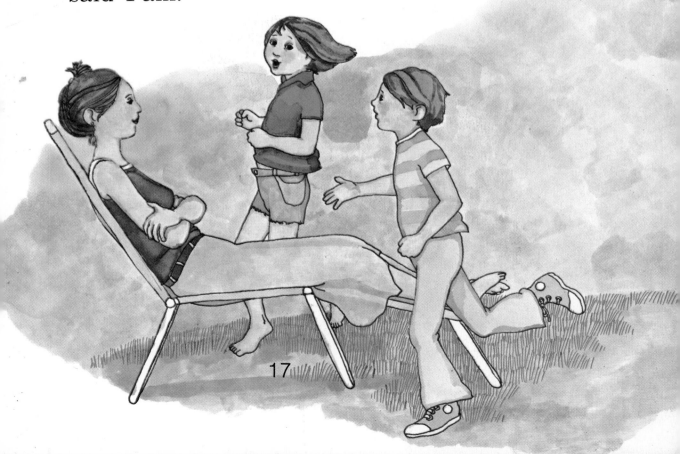

17

Pam and Ted sat down in the chairs.

Ted looked up and down.

He said, "It is very still out here, Pam."

"Yes, it is," said Pam. "But it is fun."

18

Ted looked up.
The sky was dark gray.
"It is very dark out here,"
said Ted.

Pam said, "Yes.
But it is fun."

Then they saw a bright light.
It was in the sky.
It was lightning!
Then they got wet.
Ted said, "It is very wet
out here!"

"Yes, it is," said Pam.
"And that is not fun."
They jumped up.
They ran into the house.

Ted and Pam saw Mother.
Pam said, "Please, can we sleep
in the house, Mother?"

Ted said, "The house is not
so still.
And the house is not so dark."

Pam said, "And the house is
not so wet!"

They!

The moonlight is on the park.
A cat is in the park.
Slowly, **they** go by.
The cat looks up.
The cat jumps away.
It runs into the night.
Slowly, slowly, **they** go by.

22

The moonlight is on a hill.
They come to the hill.
Slowly, slowly, **they** go uphill.
A mouse looks up in surprise.
The mouse runs into the
dark grass.

They go by the mouse.
Slowly, **they** go downhill.

The moonlight is on a pond.
Ducks are in the pond.
Slowly, **they** go by the pond.
The ducks go up into the sky.
The ducks get away fast!
Slowly, slowly, **they** go by.

24

The moonlight is on a house.
They come to the house.
They look at the house.
Then **they** go in.
Slowly, slowly, **they** go into
the house.

25

And Fay says, "That was a good party, Pam."

"Yes, it was," says Pam.

They Work at Night

Some people work in the day.
At night, they go to sleep.
But some people work at night.
They go out in the dark.
They go to work.

It is night.

A man is very sick.

The man comes here in a fast car.

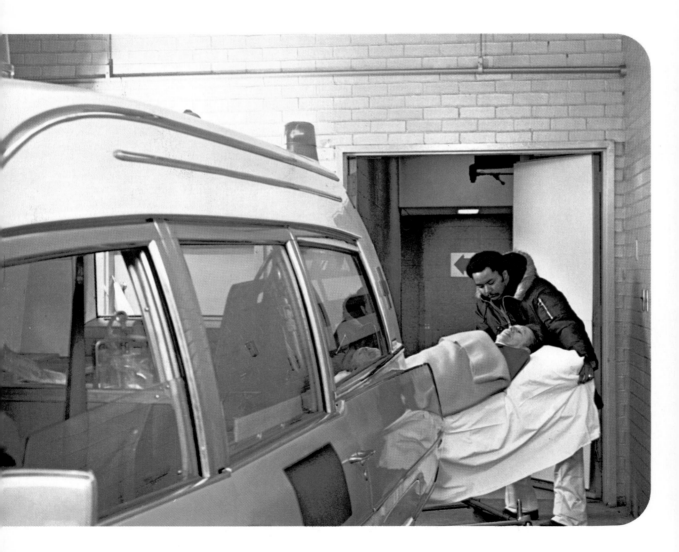

People look at the man.
They help the sick man.
Some people work at night to
help sick people.

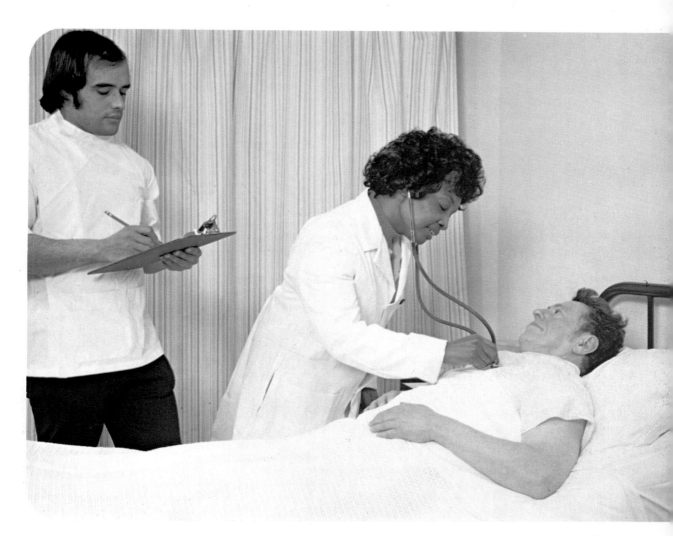

29

The hill is very dark at night.

But some people work on the hill.

They look up into the sky.

They look at the bright stars.

The people can see stars that are far, far away.

Some people work at night to look at the stars.

The dark sky lights up.
Fire!
A house is on fire!
People jump up and go to work.
They ride to the fire fast.
They put the fire out.
Some people work at night to
put out fires.
Then day comes.
And the people can go to sleep.

31

What Am I?

The Magic Hats

Pat was in the house.

It was a wet day.

So Pat said, "I'll play with the hats."

Pat got out her magic hats.

34

Pat put on a hat.

"Up I go!" she said.

"Far up into the sky.

I will ride past the last star.

Then I'll come here and land."

Pat put on her hat.

Then she was on a pond.

The land was far away.

The sky got dark.

Then lightning came.

Pat got very wet.

"I have to save the people!"
said Pat.

And at last she did!

36

Pat put on her hat.

After that, she was with some
big wagons.

She helped the people in
the wagons.

Slowly, the wagons went
over the land.

They went past dark gray hills.

Pat went on and on with
the wagons.

Then Pat's father came in.
He said, "The sun is out
at last."

"Then I will go out and play,
Dad," said Pat.
Pat put away the hats.
The magic was over.
Pat was not up in the sky.
She was not on the pond.
She was not with the wagons.
Pat was here.
Pat was Pat.
And that was that!

I'm a Fire Chief

I'm a fire chief—look out!
I'm sliding down the pole and
    into my hook and ladder.
I'm driving out of my fire station
    to a four-alarm fire.
Watch out, everybody!
There goes my siren!
I see the fire.
I'm coming up the ladder
    to save people.
I'm squirting my hose everywhere—
Sssssssssssssssssssssss.
Now the fire's out.
I put it out because I'm a fire chief!

MYRA COHN LIVINGSTON

39

When I Get Big

What will I do when I get big?
I know.
I will work on houses.
That is what I'll do.

What will I do when I get big?
I know.
I will help boys and girls.
That is what I'll do.

What will I do when I get big?
I know.
I will play in a band.
That is what I'll do.

What will I do when I get big?
I know.
I will work on the land.
That is what I'll do.
Do you know what you will do?

43

The Game

Bug went to the pond.
It sat down.
It went to sleep.
Ant came up to Bug.
Ant called, "Get up!
Get to work, Bug!"

Bug said, "Please go away.
I need some sleep."

But Ant called, "You are
a silly bug."

44

Bug said, "You say I am silly.
I am as bright as you are.
You will see.
We will play a game.
Look at me.
Then tell me what I am.
I am little, and I hop in the grass.
What am I?"

45

Ant said, "You hop in the grass?
Then you are a rabbit."

Bug said, "I am not a rabbit.
I hop in the grass, so I am a
grasshopper!"

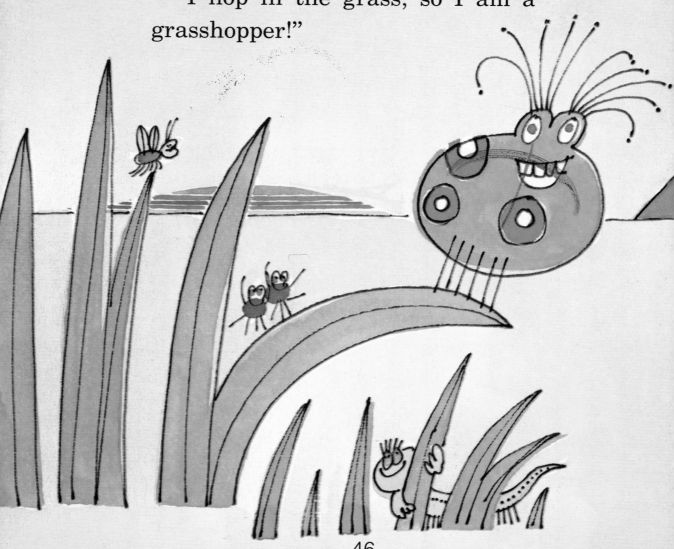

Ant said, "I am as bright as you.
I will play your game.
Tell me what I am.
I go very slowly.
But I have a house with me.
What am I?"

Bug said, "I do not know.
What are you?"

Ant called, "I am a turtle."

"You are a turtle?" said Bug.
"Then please go into your pond!"
Ant went down into the pond.
Splash!
After that, wet Ant went away.
And happy Bug went back to sleep.

What Am I?

The sky gets gray.

The day gets dark.

I light up the clouds.

The light is very bright.

Then I go away fast.

After that, the land is wet.

What am I?

I can not jump, but I can go
up and up.

I fly up into the blue sky.

I fly past the clouds.

I can fly to the moon.

What am I?

I am little.

But when I come after you,
you jump to get away.

I go to flowers.

I fly from flower to flower
in the afternoon sun.

What am I?

You can see me when you are in the sun.

I look a little like you.

I hop when you hop.

I jump when you jump.

I am still when you are still.

But you do not see me in the dark.

What am I?

You do not see me in the blue sky.

But you can see me after dark.

I look little, but I am big.

I am far, far away.

What am I?

Brad's Mask

Brad had a mask.
He put it on.
"Who will I scare with this mask?" said Brad.
"I know.
I'll scare Dad."

Father was in the house.
Brad went up to Father.
He called, "Look out!
I am the blue moonman!"

Father looked up.
"I like your mask, Brad,"
he said.
Brad did not say a thing.
Slowly he went away.

Then Brad said, "I know who
to scare.
Mother."
Brad went up to Mother.
He called, "Look out!
I am the blue moonman!"

Mother said, "Brad!
What a good mask you have!"
Brad did not say a thing.
Slowly he went away.

56

Brad said, "I did not scare her.
And I did not scare Dad."
He went into the house.
Then a moonman jumped at Brad!
"Help!" called Brad.
And he ran from the house.
Brad did not scare Father.
He did not scare Mother.
But Brad did scare Brad!

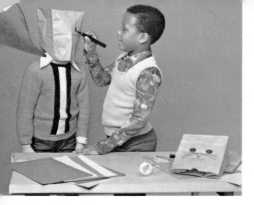

Cat and Dog Masks

You can make masks for a play.

Get some big bags.

Cut out eyes in the bags.

Cut out ears for a cat.

Put them on the bag.

Cut out ears for a dog.

Put them on the bag.

You have a cat mask.

And you have a dog mask.

You can put on a play!

The Lost Hats

For this play you will need
cat masks, dog masks, and hats.

CATS: We are sad little cats.
  Oh my, oh me!
  We have lost the birthday hats.
  Oh, me!
  We went to run
  In the morning sun.
  And we lost the hats.
  Oh, me!

They go away.

59

The dogs come in.
They have the hats.

DOGS: The cats went to play.
Oh my, oh me!
Then they all went away.
Oh, me!
And the hats were still
Up on the hill.
So we dogs have the hats,
As you see!

They go out.

Father Cat and the cats
come in.

FATHER CAT: You lost your
  birthday hats?
  Oh, my!
  Then you will have no cake!

CATS: Oh, oh, oh, oh!

FATHER CAT: No, you will have
  no cake!

Dogs come in.

DOGS: Did he say cake?
Yes, he said cake!
Oh, little cats
Who are so sad,
We have the hats!
Go tell your dad.

CATS: Oh, thank you!

62

FATHER CAT: You have the hats,
Oh little cats?
Then we will have some cake!

CATS: Oh, thank you, Dad!

FATHER CAT: Yes.
We will all have cake!

The cats put on the
birthday hats.

CATS and DOGS: The little cats
Have on the hats.
And we **all** have cake!

63

Dog Is Lost

Help Dog get back to his house.

1. Go to the flowers.
2. Then go over the pond.
3. Go up the hill, then down the hill.
4. Go to the street.
5. Find a big red house.

Did you find a house that looks like this?

Thanks! You did it!

On the Magic Hill

The Rabbit and the Bear

A rabbit was jumping up a hill in the moonlight.

She met a big bear on the hill. The bear jumped at the rabbit. "I have you!" called the bear.

"Yes, you do," said the rabbit.

66

The bear looked at the rabbit.
"I am very hungry," he said.

The rabbit sat very still.
Then she said, "Wait!
I was going to dance my
spin dance.
You will not see my fast, fast
spin dance."

The bear did like to see a good dance.

So he sat down.

"I am not so hungry," he said.

"I'll wait.

Dance your spin dance."

The rabbit did the spin dance.

Around and around she went.

"Can you dance as fast as that?"
said the rabbit.

"Yes, I can," said the bear.

The rabbit said, "No bear can
spin around as fast as I can."

"I can," said the bear.

The bear went around and around.
He was going very fast.
He did not see the rabbit.
The rabbit ran away.
She hid in the grass.
Then she looked out at the bear.
"Spin away, Bear," said the rabbit.
And the bear went around and
around and around in the moonlight.

The Grasshopper
and the Ant

In summer, the grasshopper played.
It jumped and ran in the sun.
Then it sat down and laughed
at the ant.

The ant did not sit.
In summer, the ant worked.
It was making a house.
It was filling the house with
things to eat.

At last, summer was over.

Winter came.

Snow came down from the sky.

But the ant was not sad.

The ant's house was down away
from the snow.

And the house was filled with
good things to eat.

The ant was happy in winter.

But the grasshopper was sad.
It had no house.
It did not have a thing to eat.
So it went to the ant's house.
"Little ant," it said, "please
help me.
I am hungry.
And I have to get away from
this snow."

The ant said, "In summer, I worked on my house.

Did you make a house in summer?

In summer, I filled my house with things to eat.

Did you fill your house?"

"I did not," said the grasshopper.
"In summer, I had fun.
I laughed and played in the sun."

"Is that what you did?" said the ant.
"You laughed and played in the sun?
Then laugh and play in the snow!"
With that, the ant went into
the house.

And the hungry grasshopper had
to sit in the snow.

(To be read by the teacher.)

Advice

Don't shirk
Your work
For the sake of a dream;
A fish
In the dish
Is worth ten in the stream.

Adapted by LOUIS UNTERMEYER

76

The Big Carrot

You will need people to play the

Mother Boys Cat
Little Girl Little Boy Mouse
Girls Dog Carrot

MOTHER: I need a carrot,
little girl.
Please go and pick me a
big carrot.

LITTLE GIRL: Yes, Mother.

GIRLS: So the little girl went to
pick a big carrot.
She pulled and pulled.

LITTLE GIRL: Come up, carrot!

GIRLS: But she did not get the carrot.

78

LITTLE GIRL: Mother, I cannot pick
the carrot.
It is so big I cannot pull it up.

MOTHER: I'll help you.
You pull on the carrot, and I
will pull on you.

BOYS: The girl pulled on the carrot.
The mother pulled on the girl.

MOTHER and GIRL: One, two, three, pull!

BOYS: But they did not pick the carrot.
A little boy came down the hill.
He saw them.

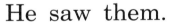

MOTHER: Will you help pick this carrot?

LITTLE BOY: Yes, I will.
   If we all pull, the carrot will come up.

GIRLS: So the girl pulled on the carrot.
   The mother pulled on the girl.
   And the boy pulled on the mother.
   They pulled and pulled.

ALL: One, two, three, pull!

GIRLS: But still, they did not pull up
   the carrot.

80

BOYS: A dog came down the hill.
It saw them.

DOG: I will help.
If we all pull, the carrot will
come up.

BOYS: So the girl pulled on the carrot.
The mother pulled on the girl.
The boy pulled on the mother.
And the dog pulled on the boy.

ALL: One, two, three, pull!

BOYS: But still, they did not pick
the carrot.

GIRLS: A cat came up to them.

CAT: I will help you.
If we all pull, the carrot will come up.

GIRLS: So the girl pulled on the carrot.
The mother pulled on the girl.
The boy pulled on the mother.
The dog pulled on the boy.
And the cat pulled on the dog.
They pulled and pulled.

ALL: One, two, three, pull!

GIRLS: But still, they did not pull up the carrot.

BOYS: A mouse came up.

MOUSE: **I** will pick that carrot!

BOYS: So the girl pulled on the carrot.
The mother pulled on the girl.
The boy pulled on the mother.
The dog pulled on the boy.
The cat pulled on the dog.
And the mouse pulled on the cat.
They pulled and pulled.

ALL: One, two, three, pull!

BOYS and GIRLS: And the carrot came up!

Carrot gets up.
All go down.

MOUSE: You see?
I pulled up the carrot!

84

The Boy Who Called Wolf

A boy sat on a hill.
He was looking after the sheep.
That was his work.
He had to save the sheep from
the hungry wolf.

85

But the boy did not like his work.

"From sun up to sun down I look after the sheep," he said.

"All I see are sheep, sheep, sheep. I never see people."

The boy got up from the grass.

He said, "I know what to do.

Today I'll play a trick.

I'll make the people come to me."

The boy tried out his trick.
He called, "Wolf, wolf!
Help!
A wolf is after the sheep!
Help!
Help!"

A man ran up the hill to the boy.
He called, "What wolf?
Tell me, and I'll get it."

But the boy said, "It was not
a wolf.

I needed to see some people.
So I played a trick."

The man said, "I do not like
people who play tricks.

Go look after the sheep.
I have work to do today."

The man went back down the hill.
The boy looked down at the man.
Then the boy tried the trick again.

He called out, "I see a wolf!
Help!
Help!"

The man called, "Are you
playing a trick again?"

The boy called, "It is a wolf!
Help me!"

89

The man ran up the hill again.
"I'll help you!" he called.
He ran up to the boy.

But the boy said, "It was not
a wolf after all.
I was still playing the trick."

The man said, "I have work to do.
I will never play this silly
game again."
He went back down the hill.
The boy looked down at the man.
And he saw a wolf!
A big wolf came up the hill.

The boy jumped up.
He called, "Help!
Help!
It **is** a wolf.
Please, help me!"
The man never looked around.

92

"This is no trick!" called
the boy.

But the man did not run back.
He went on down the hill.
He went away.
And slowly, the hungry wolf came
up the hill.

Clouds

Summer clouds are sheep clouds
Up in the sky.
Big, still sheep clouds
Slowly going by.

But winter clouds are wolf clouds.
Dark and fast they go.
Look out!
Here come wolf clouds!
And flying comes the snow!

In the City

The Bell

The boys and girls were running in the park.

They ran to the duck pond.

"Here, ducks," they called.

"Come over here."

The boys and girls played by the duck pond.

And they listened.

They listened for a bell.

Ring, ring.

Something was ringing.

The girls and boys looked.

Was this the bell that they were listening for?

No, it was not.

The boys and girls were playing in the grass.

They were hopping.

They were jumping.

And they were listening.

Something went ring, ring.

"Is that the bell?" said a boy.

"Is it?"

But it was not.

A girl said, "Who can run up
the hill fast?"

"I can!" said a boy.
They laughed and ran up the hill.

Ring, ring, ring!
Something was ringing.
The boys and girls looked.

"That is it," said a girl.
"That is the bell!"

The boys and girls ran.
They ran down the hill.
They ran to the bell.
And they were happy.

Little Red and Linda

Fun in the Park

Little Red was Linda's dog.
Linda played games with
Little Red.

She got Little Red things to eat
and drink.

Linda looked after Little Red
when he was sick.

Little Red was a very happy dog.

103

One morning, Linda called,
"Come, Little Red.

We will go to the park today."

They ran out to the street.

They went into the city park.

Linda said, "You must not run
far from me, Little Red.

If you do, you will get lost.

Do not forget."

Little Red ran to some blue flowers.
He ran back to Linda.
Then he saw two ducks.
He went after them.
The ducks ran, and so did Little Red.
Linda called, "Do not forget to
come back!"

But Little Red did forget.
He ran after the ducks.
Then the ducks hopped into a pond.
Little Red did not jump in!
He sat down.
He had a drink from the pond.
Then he saw something.
It was a cat!

Little Red tried to get the cat.
They ran past the flowers.
They ran uphill and downhill
and then out to the street.
At last the cat ran into a house.
It got away from Little Red.

Little Red looked around.
He did not see the park.
He did not see Linda.
Little Red ran up the street.
Still he did not see her.
He must go back to Linda!
He ran from street to street.
Morning went by.
But he did not find Linda.
Little Red was lost in the city.

Lost in the City

A sad little dog ran
down the gray city streets.
It was Little Red.
Where was Linda?
He did not know.
He ran into the street.
A truck went past.
"Look out, you silly dog!"
called the man in the truck.
Little Red jumped back.

109

Then a man got down from a bus.
"Come here, little dog," he said.
"I have three boys who need a dog like you."
But Little Red did not go to the man.
He ran down the street.

Little Red needed things to eat
and drink.

He saw a bag by a house.
He went over to the bag.

A girl and a boy saw Little Red.
The girl said, "Are you hungry,
little dog?
Just come with us.
We will get you something to eat."
But Little Red did not go with them.
He ran down the street into a park.

111

The sun was just going down.
It was going to get dark.
Little Red was sad.
He must find Linda!

Two boys came up to Little Red.
"Are you lost?" said one boy.
"Come with us.
We have just the house for you."
But Little Red did not go with
the boys.
He ran up a hill.

At last Little Red had to sit down.
He did not know what to do.
Then, his ears went up.
He listened.
A girl was calling.
She was calling, "Little Red!
Where are you?"
Who was it?
It was Linda!

Little Red ran down the hill.

He ran up to Linda and jumped on her.

Linda said, "Oh, Little Red! You came back!

Where did you go?

Oh, it is so good to see you again!"

Little Red was so happy to see Linda.

He was very hungry, but he was happy.

He was back with Linda again!

(To be read by the teacher.)

My Dog

His nose is short and scrubby;
    His ears hang rather low;
And he always brings the stick back,
    No matter how far you throw.

He gets spanked rather often
    For things he shouldn't do,
Like lying-on-beds, and barking,
    And eating up shoes when they're new.

He always wants to be going
    Where he isn't supposed to go.
He tracks up the house when it's snowing—
    Oh, puppy, I love you so.

MARCHETTE CHUTE

115

116

What Is a City?

What is a city?

It is streets.

It is cars and buses and trucks.

It is buildings.

And a city is people.

Many people are in a city.

117

Many buildings are in a city.
They look like boxes.
Some buildings are very big,
and some buildings are very little.

Many buses, trucks, and cars
are in a city.

Blue cars, red cars, trucks, and
buses wait at the light.

Then, away they go, down the
city street.

Many people work in a city.
In the morning, people get up.
They ride to the city.
They go to work.

120

In the afternoon, people go up
and down the city streets.
They sit and eat lunch.
They go for rides on the buses.
And they look at things in the
big buildings.

121

At night, many people go from the city.

Work is over.

Many lights go out.

The big buildings get dark.

The city is still.

Fun in the City

Boys and girls can have fun in the city parks.

The parks in the city are good for games.

Girls and boys go to a big building.

They see animals.

Some animals are little.

But just look at the big animals!

124

Many boys and girls wait until some trucks come to the street.

The trucks have rides.

The trucks have games to play.

The girls and boys get good things to eat and drink.

They have so much fun!

Many people are here today.
Boys and girls come.
They look at people.
They look at beautiful things.
They smell good things to eat.
They sit and have lunch.
They go up and down the street until night comes.
Girls and boys have so much to do in the city!

126

(To be read by the teacher.)

In the City

The buildings are tall,
The people are small
In the city, in the city.

The noises are loud,
There's always a crowd
In the city, in the city.

The cars move fast,
The trucks jolt past;
Up in the sky the pigeons fly.

East or West,
I like it best
In the city, in the city.

LOIS LENSKI

127

Dog Cleans Up

Dog is cleaning up the house.

No, no, Dog!

That bear cannot go in the jar.

Where can it go?

Will you help Dog?

Tell Dog where to put all his things.

128

Carrots, Potatoes, Peas, and Tomatoes

Victor Helps Out

One day, Jack was planting things.
"Can I help?" said Victor.

Jack said, "You are much too little."

"I am not," said Victor.

Jack said, "We will see.
Yes, you can help me."

So Victor helped Jack.

He helped plant peas.

He helped plant carrot seeds.

He helped plant tomatoes and potatoes.

And he helped Jack to look after the seeds.

131

One summer day, a little plant came up.

Then little plants came up all around it.

Jack said, "Come, Victor.

Today the plants need water."

So Victor helped Jack to water the plants.

132

Then, weeds came up.

They were all around the plants.

Jack said, "We have to pull up the weeds, too, Victor."

So Victor helped Jack to pull up the weeds.

Day after day, Jack and Victor looked after the plants.

All the plants got big.

The tomatoes got big.

The potatoes got big.

The carrots got big.

And the peas got big.

One day, Jack said, "The tomatoes are big and red.

We can pick some, Victor."

So Victor helped Jack to pick the tomatoes.

Victor looked at the tomatoes.
He said, "They are so beautiful!
And I helped you with them, Jack."

Jack said, "Yes, you did.
Thank you, Victor."

135

Then they went into the house.
"I'll make us some lunch.
I'll make tomato soup," said Jack.
Victor did not help Jack to
make the soup.
He was too little for that.
But he did help Jack to eat it.
And it was very good soup!

136

Growing Things

You can see a plant grow.
Just get a seed like this.

Put it in a jar.

Wet the seed.

Soon the seed will grow.

Seeds like this grow until
they are big plants.

Tomatoes, too, grow from seeds.

They grow slowly into little plants.

The tomato plants need water.

This plant did not get water.

Tomato plants need light from the sun.

This plant got too little light.

138

Tomato plants grow and grow.
Soon the plants are very big.
They have many little flowers.

The flowers go away.
And soon the plants have many
little green tomatoes.

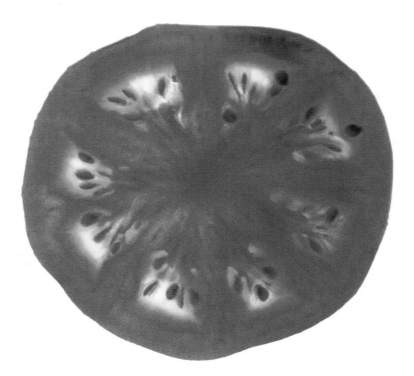

The tomatoes grow until they are big and red.

People pick them from the plants. The tomatoes are good to eat.

What is in a tomato?
You can find out.
Get one and eat it.
What do you see in the tomato?
Many little tomato seeds.

Some people save the seeds for planting.

The seeds grow into new tomato plants.

The plants have many new green tomatoes.

The green tomatoes grow into big red tomatoes.

And the people eat them!

(To be read by the teacher.)

Maytime Magic

A little seed
For me to sow . . .

A little earth
To make it grow . . .
A little hole,
A little pat . . .
A little wish,
And that is that.

A little sun,
A little shower . . .
A little while,
And then—a flower!

MABEL WATTS

142

Birthday Soup

by
Else Holmelund Minarik

Pictures by Maurice Sendak

Adapted from *Little Bear*,
written by
Else Holmelund Minarik

"Mother Bear.

Mother Bear.

Where are you?" calls Little Bear.

"Oh, my, Mother Bear is not here.

And today is my birthday."

"Soon my friends will come.

But I do not see a birthday cake.

Oh, my, no birthday cake.

What can I do?

The pot is by the fire.

The water in the pot is hot.

If I put something in the water,

I can make Birthday Soup.

All my friends like soup.

Let me see what we have.

We have carrots and potatoes,

peas and tomatoes.

I can make soup with carrots,

potatoes, peas, and tomatoes."

So Little Bear makes soup in the
big black pot.

Hen comes in.

"Happy Birthday, Little Bear,"
she says.

"Thank you, Hen," says Little Bear.

Hen says, "My!
Something smells good here.
Is it in the big black pot?"

"Yes," says Little Bear.
"I am making Birthday Soup.
Will you wait and have some?"

"Oh, yes.
Thank you," says Hen.
And she sits down to wait.

Then, Duck comes in.

"Happy Birthday, Little Bear,"
says Duck.

"My, something smells good.
Is it in the big black pot?"

"Thank you, Duck," says Little Bear.

"Yes, I am making Birthday Soup.

Will you wait and have some with us?"

"Thank you, yes, thank you," says Duck.

And she sits down to wait.

Then, Cat comes in.

"Happy Birthday, Little Bear,"
he says.

"Thank you, Cat," says Little Bear.

"Do you like Birthday Soup?

I am making Birthday Soup."

Cat says, "**Can** you cook?

If you **can** make it, I will eat it."

"Good," says Little Bear.

"The Birthday Soup is hot.

So we must eat it.

We cannot wait for Mother Bear.

I do not know where she is."

"Here is some soup for you, Hen,"
says Little Bear.

"And here is some soup for
you, Duck."

"And here is some soup for you, Cat.

And here is some soup for me.

We can all have some Birthday Soup."

Cat sees Mother Bear and says,

"Wait, Little Bear.

Do not eat.

Shut your eyes and say one, two, three."

Little Bear shuts his eyes and
says, "One, two, three."

Mother Bear comes in with
a big cake.

"Look," says Cat.

"Oh, Mother Bear," says Little Bear.

"What a big beautiful Birthday Cake!

Birthday Soup is good to eat,

but not as good as Birthday Cake.

I am so happy you did not forget."

"Yes, Happy Birthday, Little Bear!"

says Mother Bear.

"This Birthday Cake is a surprise

for you.

I never did forget your birthday,

and I never will."

PAGES 7-10

Stan
dark
light
lightning
have
jar
sky
star

PAGES 12-16

night
gray
like
eye
bright
owl
your

PAGES 17-21

sleep
out
please
fun

mother
Pam

PAGES 22-26

moonlight
slowly
run
by
uphill
downhill
come
say

PAGES 27-31

some
day
people
work
man
sick
far
fire

PAGES 34-38

her
land

last
past
father
dad

PAGES 40-43

what
when
do
know
boy
girl

PAGES 44-48

ant
call
silly
am
as
game
back

PAGES 49-53

cloud
blue
moon

fly
flower

PAGES 54-57

Brad
mask
who
scare
moonman
thing

PAGE 58

cut
bag
them
make
ear

PAGES 59-63

sad
oh
my
birthday
were
all
no

cake
thank

PAGES 66-70

bear
hungry
wait
spin
dance
around

PAGES 71-75

summer
laugh
sit
fill
making
eat
winter
snow

PAGES 77-84

carrot
pick
pull
one

two
three
if

PAGES 85-93

sheep
wolf
never
today
trick
tried
again

PAGES 98-102

listen
bell
something
ring

PAGES 103-108

drink
Linda
red
street
forget
must
city

```
        9
C       0
D       1
E       2
F       3
G       4
H       5
I       6
J       7
```

Unit openers, pages 5, 33, 65, 97, 129: Oni
Angela Adams: 130-136; Penny Carter: 127; Diane de Groat: 7-10; Len Ebert: 40-43; Rosalind Fry: 59-63; Abner Graboff: 44-47; Leigh Grant: 17-21, 22-26; Tad Krumeich: 116-122; Dora Leder: 115; Ronald LeHew: 76; Don Madden: 34-38, 54-57; Carol Nicklaus: 66-70; Jan Pyk: 49-53; Elaine Raphael and Don Bolognese: 78-84; Ruth Sanderson: 103-114; Maurice Sendak: 143-157; Sylvia Stone: 39, 98-102, 123-126; Maggie Swanson: 11, 142; Kyuzo Tsugami: 71-75; Hans Zander: 85-93.

All photographs are HARBRACE except those listed below: KEY: t, (top); b, (bottom); r, (right); l, (left)

Page 6, Peter Miller/Photo Researchers; 12, Louise and Paul Dana/DPI; 13, Clyde H. Smith/Peter Arnold; 14, G. Holton/Photo Researchers; 15, N. and M. Jansen; 30, Hale Observatory; 31(r), Bendick Associates/Monkmeyer; 77, Victoria Beller-Smith; 94, Russ Kinne/Photo Researchers; 95, L. G. Wishart/Photo Researchers; 118, Tom Hollyman/Photo Researchers; 119, Don Morgan/Photo Researchers; 120, Mimi Forsyth/Monkmeyer; 121, J. A. Brown/Shostal; 122, Porterfield Chickering/Photo Researchers; 139(tr), Noble Proctor/Photo Researchers; (tl), Syd Greenberg/Photo Researchers; (b), Grant Heilman; 140, Runk/Schoenberger for Grant Heilman; 141(both), Grant Heilman.

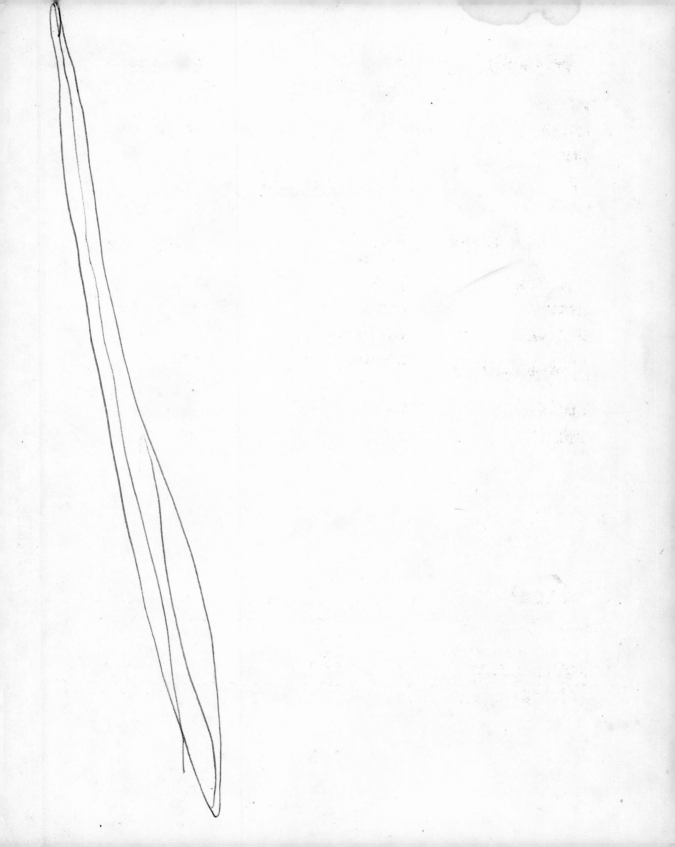